Workbook Answer Key

1 Name

Grammar

1

a present perfect
b simple past
c simple present
d future *(be) going to*
e present perfect
f future *(be) going to*
g simple past
h present progressive

2

a His parents did not give him a typical Mexican name.
b He has never broken the law.
c He did not go on vacation last year.
d I am going to have coffee after the class.
e I do not have my purse with me right now.
f She does not want to see me.
g She is reading a book about Hawaii.
h They are learning English for their work.
i We have never been to New York.

3

a Dave and I don't live in the same town.
b He doesn't know me very well.
c He can't understand my problems.
d He hasn't done very well in his job.
e Our parents weren't very good friends.
f We didn't go to the same school.
g We aren't thinking about getting married.
h We aren't going to have a big party.

4

a He always looks ~~like~~ terrible early in the morning.
b ✓
c ✓
d They looked ~~like~~ tired after the class.
e ✓
f She looks ~~like~~ foreign – is she Brazilian?
g ✓
h You look ~~like~~ very stressed. What's wrong?
i The teacher looks ~~like~~ very young.

5

a Have you ever been to the USA?
b What are you wearing today?
c What kind of things do you read?
d How often do you use your smartphone?
e How many people are there in your class?
f When did you last have an English class?
g How many years are you going to study English?

6

a What are you holding in your hand?
b ✓
c Who did you see last night?
d ✓
e How much money do you have in your pocket?
f How many brothers do you have?
g ✓

Vocabulary

1

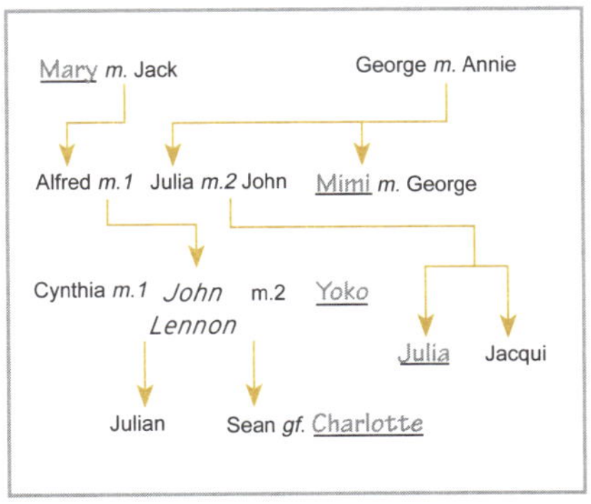

2

a F
b T
c F
d F
e F
f T
g T
h F

3

1 first
2 last name
3 middle
4 maiden
5 initials
6 husband
7 nicknames

4

1	2	3	4	5	6	7	8
c	e	a	f	b	h	g	d

5

1 short
2 blond
3 eyes
4 beard
5 good-looking
6 beautiful smile
7 cute
8 medium-length
9 straight
10 brown

6

1 Really?
2 Do they?
3 That sounds great.
4 Great!
5 I've never heard of him.
6 Wow!

Pronunciation

2

a What's the word order for negatives?
b I'm going to have coffee after the class.
c Write new vocabulary on a piece of paper.
d My brother is going to be a banker.

2 The World

Grammar

1

a castle
b destination
c bridge
d vacation
e office
f tooth

2

1 such
2 so
3 so
4 such
5 such
6 so
7 such

3

a had a great afternoon
b don't like it
c bought lot of things
d we asked for another one
e caught their plane
f you're breaking the law
g happy there
h didn't go swimming

4

a much
b many
c many
d much
e many
f much
g many
h much

6

a much
b enough
c a lot of
d not enough
e too much
f Not many
g a little
h Many

7

a	b	c	d	e	f	g
7	3	2	6	1	4	5

Vocabulary

1

a statue
b beach
c square
d hill
e canal
f high-rise
g fountain
h library

2

1 exciting
2 big
3 great
4 fantastic
5 spectacular
6 beautiful
7 friendly
8 welcoming
9 modern
10 crowded
11 noisy
12 polluted
13 humid
14 dull
15 fabulous
16 expensive
17 cheap
18 romantic

3

a Mexican
b Japanese
c Italian
d Chilean
e Portuguese
f Egyptian
g Brazilian
h Argentinian
i Canadian

4

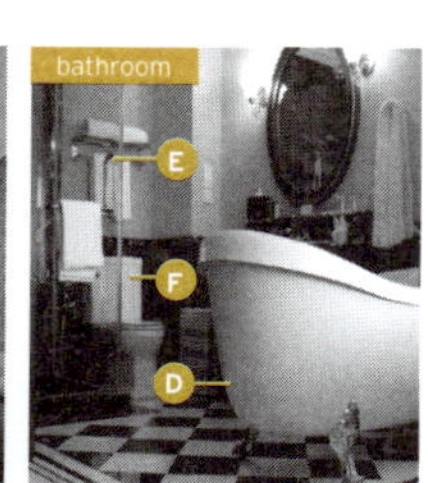

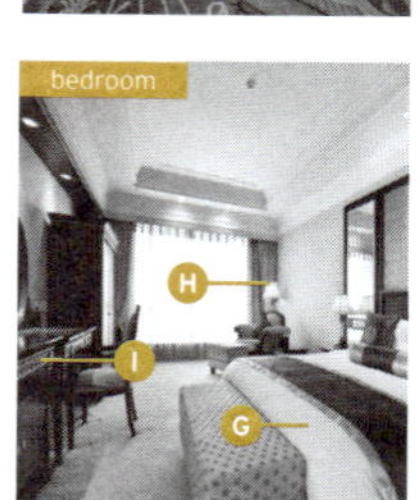

A TV
B rug
C couch
D bathtub
E shower
F toilet
G bed
H lamp
I desk
J stove
K sink
L table
M chair

5

a Palermo
b Messina
c Mount Etna
d Enna
e Catania
f Siracusa
g Ragusa
h Agrigento

Pronunciation

1

a come
b neighbor
c money
d honey

2

/oʊ/	/aʊ/	/ɔɪ/
coast	how	boy
don't	noun	coin
hotel	outside	enjoy
most	south	noise
phone	town	voice

Listening

1

Marrakech, Morocco (picture b)

2

a F
b F
c F
d F

e F

f F

g T

h T

i F

j F

a He first went to Marrakech 10 or 12 years ago.

b He went there for a long weekend.

c He traveled with his best friend, Dave.

d He stayed with the family of a colleague.

e After dinner, he visited the main square.

f Djemaa el Fna is the name of the main square.

i He has been there 10 or 12 times.

j His last visit was three years ago.

3 Love

Grammar

1

G	L	E	C	M	N	R	C	M	X	Z	E	P	I	U	B	H	P	H	E	N	Y	S	M	V
Y	E	D	U	U	K	H	U	B	Q	Q	S	B	E	G	A	N	I	S	K	I	B	X	E	R
Q	G	R	T	K	I	M	U	I	R	H	E	A	W	M	Q	V	E	I	W	A	L	X	T	R
U	Q	M	M	N	D	X	X	C	I	L	U	H	C	Z	Z	N	R	H	O	P	U	T	W	S
S	B	K	E	A	R	F	H	J	J	G	G	O	P	Y	A	I	U	E	J	S	V	U	B	M
L	V	S	Z	P	A	C	P	N	T	X	U	A	I	P	G	T	S	W	A	M	I	S	R	B
E	E	N	N	D	N	Y	H	L	H	U	T	O	A	N	H	A	U	V	E	G	M	H	O	G
P	L	I	Z	A	K	B	U	I	O	S	R	J	K	F	G	L	H	K	D	A	Q	R	U	Y
T	O	O	K	W	M	C	S	T	U	A	O	C	A	U	G	H	T	X	Z	M	I	P	G	G
G	Q	Y	R	N	I	R	N	F	G	A	P	G	M	K	V	A	F	V	S	B	M	A	H	R
O	C	S	V	Y	W	X	E	H	H	C	M	D	V	C	A	N	U	D	R	Z	T	L	T	R
A	C	A	M	E	Y	G	F	G	T	E	R	Z	F	C	T	A	U	G	H	T	N	N	U	K

2

a began

b brought

c caught

d came

e cut

f drank

g put

h lit

i met

j slept

k swam

l took

m taught

n thought

3

a Did you go shopping yesterday?

b Was it cold yesterday?

c Did you enjoy your last vacation?

d When was your last English class?

e Where did you go on vacation last year?

f What did you have for dinner last night?

g Who were your best friends in elementary school?

4

a Juliet wasn't a happy girl.

b Juliet's family and Romeo's family weren't friends.

c They didn't want her to marry him.

d Juliet wasn't in love with Paris, a friend of her family.

e She didn't like him.

f Juliet didn't know what to do.

g She didn't tell her parents about her true feelings.

5

a was wearing

b was holding

c was feeling

d was sitting

e were speaking

f was getting

g were planning

6

1 was going

2 was watching

3 said

4 opened

5 was sitting

6 began

7 wanted

8 was raining

9 decided

10 arrived

7

a regularly

b attractively

c beautifully

d early

e fast

f happily

g loudly

8

a careful

b badly

c quietly

d quickly

e neat

f angry

g well

h different

Vocabulary

1

1 liked

2 flirt

3 called

4 date

5 kissed

6 was

7 have

8 meet

2

1 live

2 move

3 get

4 had

5 split

6 lost

3

a ~~Oh, I do.~~

b ~~Neither did I.~~

c ~~Oh, I didn't.~~

d ~~Me, too.~~

4

1 One day

2 At first

3 Then

4 That evening

5 Finally

6 That night

7 The next morning

5

a relaxed

b scared

c tired

d embarrassed

e bored

f annoyed

g surprised

h confused

6

a Don't you like the movie?

b She talked about me when I was a child.

c He was wearing a Dracula costume.

d They had a late night last night.
e He was very hard to understand.
f She wanted a lot more information.

7

a to work
b dark
c better
d divorced
e together
f tickets
g changed
h along

Pronunciation

2

a /wər/
b /wəz/
c /wəz/
d /wɑz/
e /wər/
f /wɜr/

Writing

1

A 2
B 3
C 1

2

a After stealing a car, they drove out of town.
b After driving for a few miles, they realized they needed gas.
c Before killing the garage attendant, they filled the car with gas.
d Before driving away, they stole money from the garage.

4 Shopping

Grammar

1

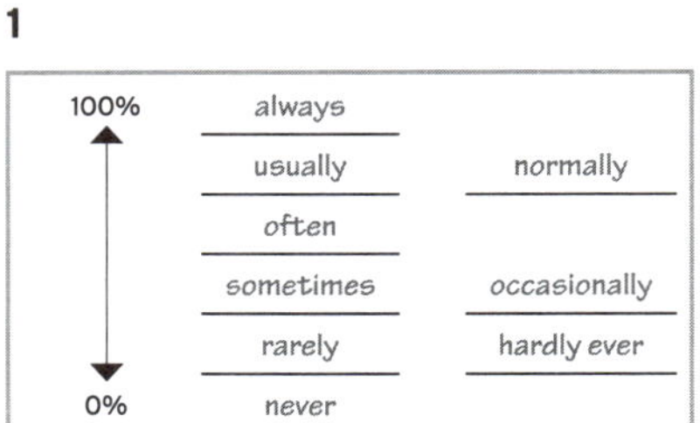

2

a I am always on a diet.
b I hardly ever wear perfume.
c I often buy second-hand clothes.
d I don't usually like gold jewelry.
e Shopping is rarely a pleasure.
f I always get changed after work.
g My shoes are sometimes dirty.
h I am normally good at choosing gifts.

3

a for
b to
c to
d for
e for
f to
g to
h to

4

a I think I'll buy her some perfume.
b I told them a story.
c I let her my car.
d He made her a delicious meal.
e Why don't you get her some chocolate?
f He showed him/her his wedding album.
g Give her/him the ticket.
h I sent him/her an email last week.

5

a cooking
b to study
c to finish
d spending
e to lend
f to take off
g going
h to have

6

1 to try
2 watching
3 choosing
4 spending
5 to go
6 to get
7 to be
8 talking
9 to eat

7

a Do you come
b Are you listening
c Do most of your friends work
d Does it rain
e Are the students in your class studying
f Do you read
g Does your father
h Is it getting

Vocabulary

1

a a can of paint
b a bunch of grapes
c a box of matches
d a pair of scissors
e a pack of gum
f a piece of cake
g a bottle of perfume
h a jar of mayonnaise

2

a patterned
b floral
c pinstriped
d striped
e checked
f plain

3

a	b	c	d	e	f	g	h
4	2	6	1	3	7	8	5

4

a skirt, jacket, pantyhose
b pajamas
c tie, shirt, suit
d dress, shoes, scarf, hat
e coat, gloves, hat

Pronunciation

1

/eɪ/	/aɪ/
always	decide
brain	mind
exchange	right
great	striped
pay	style
plain	surprise
same	try

2

Listening

1

The speakers are talking about c)

2

1 b
2 c
3 a
4 b
5 c
6 b

5 In shape

Grammar

1

Adjective	Comparative	Superlative
good	better	best
near	nearer	nearest
wet	wetter	wettest
easy	easier	easiest
far	farther	farthest
dangerous	more dangerous	most dangerous

2

a Basketball isn't as dangerous as skiing.
b Judo isn't as interesting as tennis.
c Women are better at ball games than men.
d Swimming is not as good for you as running.
e The rules of basketball are easier to understand than the rules of volleyball.
f Playing a sport is not as exciting as watching it.
g Being in shape is more important for younger people than it is for older people.

3

a The heaviest
b The biggest
c The most crowded
d the wettest
e The hottest
f the most expensive
g the noisiest
h the fastest

4

The most dangerous age for a man's health is from 50 to 60. Exercise is very important, but not as important as a healthy diet. A bad diet is the biggest reason for health problems. Vegetables are better than fast food, for example. People with the most stressful jobs have a shorter life than people who have no stress. They should try to relax. They should exercise more than once a week. A hard, sweaty sport is not as good for your health as regular, easy exericse.

5

a has given up coffee
b hang up your clothes
c deal with problems
d look up words
e taken care of a baby
f filled in a form
g throw away old love letters
h make up an excuse
i get along with the people

6

a Don't forget to turn it off.
b I take after him.
c My grandparents brought her up.
d He decided to give it up.
e Please put them away.
f The children cleared it up.
g We had to call it off.

Vocabulary

1

a	b	c	d	e	f	g	h
2	4	1	3	6	8	5	7

2

Suggested answers:

a fast
b well
c often
d much
e long
f far
g old
h many

3

a five hundred
b point five
c three quarters
d one point seven five
e seven thousand, one hundred and eighty-four
f three-nil
g one and a half

4

a ~~his neighbors~~
b ~~shoes~~
c ~~car~~
d ~~a novel~~
e ~~keys~~
f ~~the office~~

5

a run after
b clear; up
c deal with
d fill in
e take after
f get along with
g bring up
h look; up

6

a Sports: golf, skiing, soccer
b People: golfer, runner, skier
c Places: court, field, swimming pool
d Equipment: goggles, helmet, net

7

a Dont be mean!
b Don't worry.
c Come back!
d Be patient.
e Try again.
f Be careful!

8

1 goes
2 goes
3 does

4 plays
5 plays
6 does
7 does
8 plays
9 goes

Writing

1

1 Paragraph C
2 Paragraph A
3 Paragraph B

2

a 5
b 7
c 4
d 6
e 2
f 3
g 1

3

a Although we arrived early, there was a very long line.
b Although the tickets were very expensive, we didn't have a very good view.
c The match was very exciting, although it was very long.
d Although nothing much happened in the first half, the second half was fantastic.
e Chivas won the game, although they were not the better team. / Although Chivas won the game, they were not the better team.
f I enjoyed the game, although my friends thought it was boring. / Although I enjoyed the game, my friends thought it was boring.

Pronunciation

1

first	windsurf
third	work
turn	worst

course	sport
court	more
score	for / four

2

/ɜr/	/ɔr/
earn	board
person	form
serve	morning
thirst	story

6 Job

Grammar

1

1 a flight attendant
2 an au pair

2

a Does she have to wear a uniform at work?
b Can she travel to different countries for free?
c Does she have to have a college education?
d Can she sit down much in her job?
e Does she have to pay for somewhere to live?
f Can she wear her own clothes?
g Does she have to like young children?
h Can she invite her friends to dinner?

3

a Yes, she does. / No, she doesn't.
b Yes, she can. / No, she can't.
c Yes, she does. / No, she doesn't.
d Yes, she can. / No, she can't.
e Yes, she does. / No, she doesn't.
f Yes, she can. / No, she can't.
g Yes, she does. / No, she doesn't.
h Yes, she can. / No, she can't.

4

a has she had
b 's had
c Have you ever worked
d 've never been
e 've ever eaten
f 've liked
g 've always wanted

5

a Have you ever been on TV?
b Have you ever worked as an au pair?
c Have your parents ever forgotten your birthday?
d Has your teacher ever made a joke in class?
e Have you ever seen a ballet?
f Have you ever voted in a political election?
g Have you ever ridden a motorcycle?

6

1 have had
2 have ever had
3 started
4 needed
5 have ever made
6 didn't like
7 felt
8 was
9 sold
10 said
11 didn't sell
12 decided

7

a when I was eighteen
b this week
c yesterday
d last summer
e recently
f today
g over the years

Vocabulary

1

a pilot
b farmer
c soldier
d au pair
e flight attendant
f engineer
g surgeon
h butcher
i DJ

2

a actor
b tour guide
c CEO
d vet
e archaeologist
f cook
g telesales person

3

a a day
b permission
c a decision
d a break

e two weeks
f a living
g a part-time job
h money

4

a find
b take
c take
d take
e make
f lose
g ask
h make

5

a	b	c	d	e	f	g
7	4	5	6	1	3	2

Listening

1

They describe c) and f)

2

5

6

3

1

7

2

4

3

Game 1

1 Yes
2 Yes
3 Yes
4 No
5 No
6 -
7 No

Game 2

1 Yes
2 No
3 Yes
4 –
5 No
6 Yes
7 Yes

Notes

ISBN 9786685732405

9 786685 732405